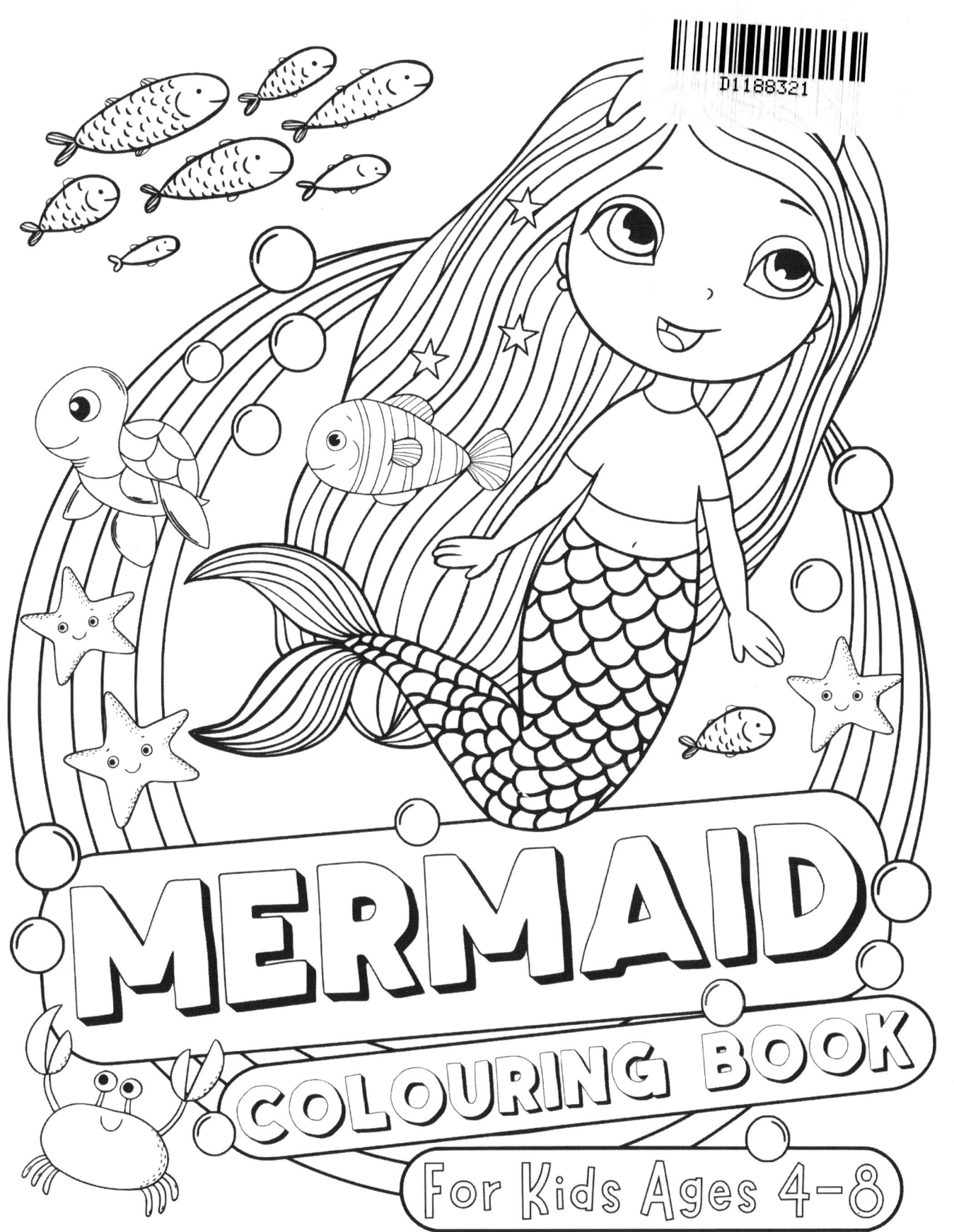

MERMAID

COLOURING BOOK

For Kids Ages 4-8

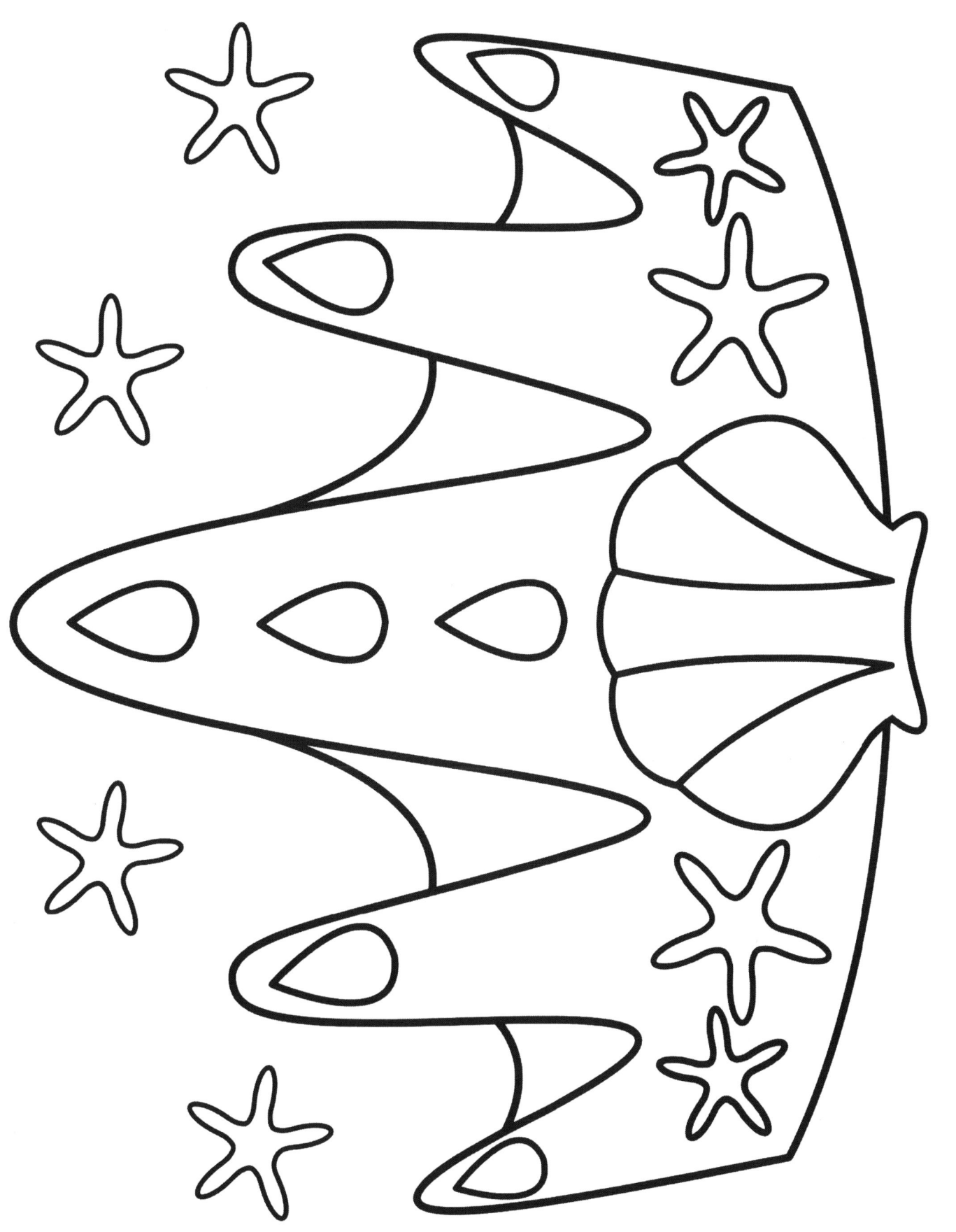

MERMAID FOREVER

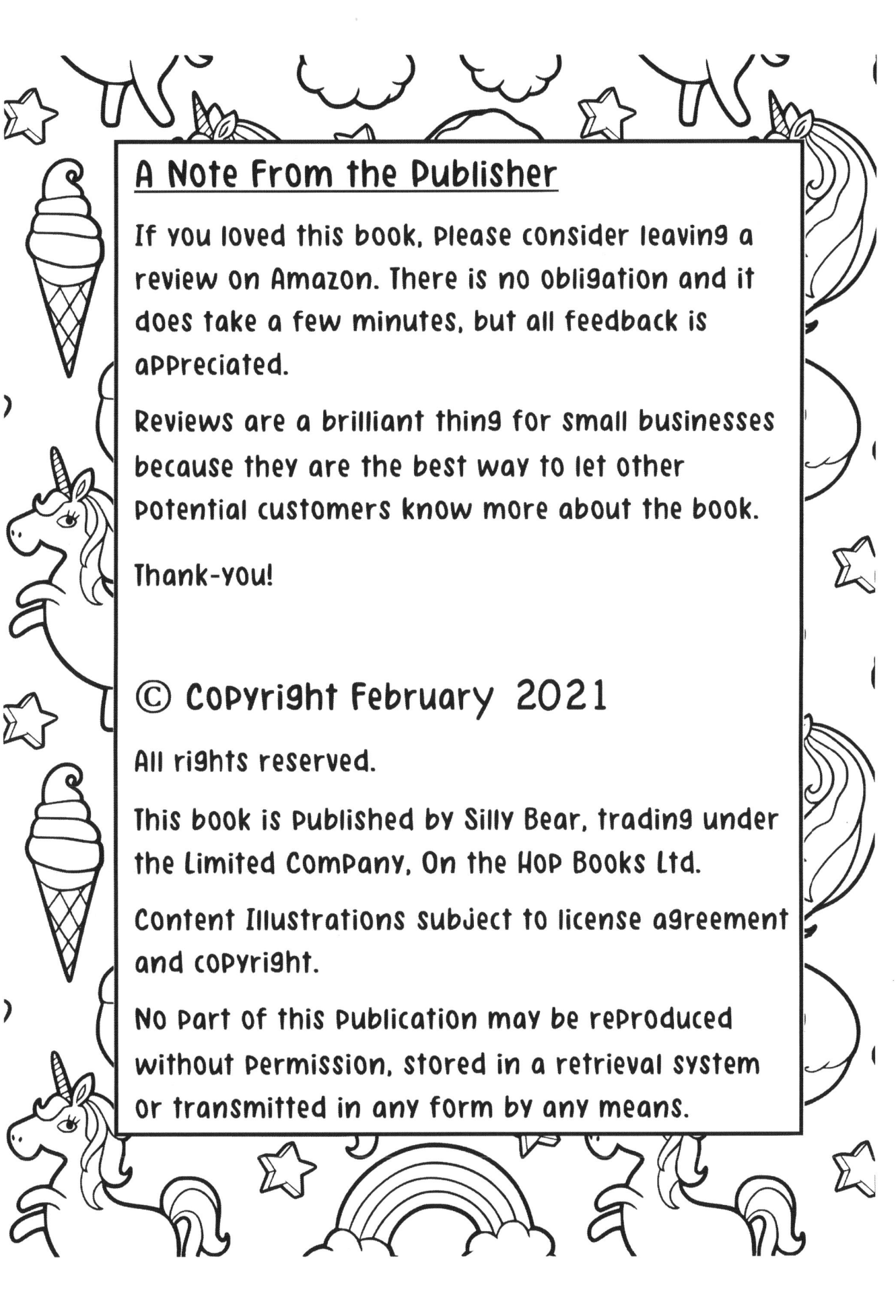

A Note From the Publisher

If you loved this book, please consider leaving a review on Amazon. There is no obligation and it does take a few minutes, but all feedback is appreciated.

Reviews are a brilliant thing for small businesses because they are the best way to let other potential customers know more about the book.

Thank-you!

Printed in Great Britain
by Amazon